What you need

Supplies for creative activities

Getting started

The activities in this book use things you can find at home, or that can be bought from art supply shops. Some of the most commonly-used materials are shown here, but always check the 'You will need' section at the start of each activity before you begin.

Chopping board

Paints

Cookie cutters

Spoon

Glass bowls

Tracing paper

Card

Coloured paper

White paper

Tape (single & double-sided)

Ruler

Pencils

Colouring pens

Cooling rack

Smart Kids
Activity

priddy books
big ideas for little people

Contents

Note to parents

This book is full of creative ideas that will help you make the most of the spare time that you spend with your children. These activities will ease the boredom of a rainy day spent indoors, and encourage your child's creativity and imagination.

This edition copyright © 2009 St. Martin's Press, LLC
Originally published as My Big Creative Activity Book
copyright © 2004

Published by

priddy☺books

4 Crinan Street, London, N1 9XW
A division of Macmillan Publishers Ltd.

Cotton thread and needles

Pins

Crayons

Mini muffin tin

Coloured felt

Pair of compasses

Pinking shears

Scissors

Glue

String

Paintbrushes

Flexible wire

Safety first

Children will be able to complete many of the activities in this book by themselves, but some of them will require adult supervision and assistance. We have made it clear which things should be done specifically by an adult.

5

Animal masks

Creative creature disguises

You will need:

- coloured felt
- large sheet of card
- scissors • pencil
- tracing paper
- paintbrush
- elastic • needle
- glue • pen
- templates supplied

1 Trace the eyepiece template onto card and cut out. Copy this onto a piece of felt.

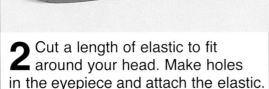

2 Cut a length of elastic to fit around your head. Make holes in the eyepiece and attach the elastic.

3 Cut out the felt shape and glue it to the card eyepiece.

4 Trace the templates of your choice from pages 7 or 8 to make the rest of your chosen mask.

5 Copy the shapes onto felt and cut them out.

6 Glue the felt shapes onto the card pieces.

7 Glue the shapes together to make the masks. Look at the finished masks to see how.

Trace over these templates to make the shapes for the masks

Eyepiece
(use this shape for all three of the masks)

Trunk

Ears (x2)

Tusks (x2)

Elephant

Cut white strips to add to the trunk

Nose

Mouth

Snout

Ears (x2)

Eyes (x2)

Panda

Nose

Nostrils

Ears (x2)

Mouth

Inner ears (x2)

Pig

8

Tissue pom-poms

A fun way to celebrate a special occasion

You will need:

- at least 18 sheets of tissue paper (various colours)
- lollipop sticks
- scissors
- tape

Do not cut all the way

1 Place three sheets of tissue paper together. Fold in half lengthways and cut 3-cm wide strips as shown.

2 Starting at one end, roll the folded edge around the end of the lollipop stick and secure with tape.

Remember to secure each tissue strip to the stick with tape

3 Repeat three more times per pom-pom, wrapping each new tissue strip around the previous one.

4 These pom-poms are perfect for celebrating sports day, birthdays and all kinds of special occasions. They are also great for practising to be a cheerleader!

Paper roses

Make some pretty paper flowers

You will need:

- 75-cm x 8-cm piece of yellow crêpe paper
- sheet of green crêpe paper
- flexible wire
- cotton thread
- cotton wool
- pencil • scissors
- glue

1 Cut a 15-cm piece of flexible wire. Add a piece of cotton wool to one end and glue yellow paper around it.

2 Fold the yellow paper in half crossways, then fold it the same way three more times.

3 Draw a curve around the edge of the paper as shown. Cut around it and unfold the paper.

4 Wrap the petals around the wire and tie cotton thread around the base of the flower.

5 Cut leaf shapes from the green paper. Glue an 8-cm piece of flexible wire between two shapes.

6 Make three to four leaves in this way. Wind the leaf wires around the rose stem.

7 Cover the stem and the leaf wires with a strip of green paper. Glue the end of the paper in place.

These paper roses make
a wonderful springtime
decoration or Mother's Day gift

Scented pillows

Make a sweet-smelling present

You will need:

- 20-cm x 10-cm piece of white felt
- 8-cm x 8-cm piece of pink felt
- lavender or similar dried, scented flowers
- scissors • ribbon
- sewing needle
- cotton thread
- fabric glue

1 Cut the white felt in half crossways. Cut the pink felt into a heart shape.

2 Sew around the edge of the heart for decoration. Glue it to one of the white squares.

3 Place the two white squares together and sew around three sides, leaving one open.

4 Fill the bag with the lavender. Place a piece of ribbon in one corner to make a loop and secure it in place with fabric glue. Sew up the remaining side of the pillow.

Try different fabrics

Or the first letter of a name

A pretty flower

Or a Valentine's gift?

13

Scanner art

Use a computer to decorate your things

You will need:

- computer
- scanning software
- scanner • colour printer
- coloured paper • ruler
- storage containers
- objects to scan
- paintbrush
- glue • scissors

1 Choose the objects that you wish to scan and the colour of paper you would like to use.

2 Choose a container for the objects. Measure it and make a note of its size.

3 Place the objects on the scanner. Put the paper above them and scan them into your computer.

4 Check that the size of the image is big enough to cover the container you are using.

5 Print out your picture in colour. Make sure that you are happy with it.

6 Cut out the picture to the correct size if necessary.

7 Carefully glue the picture to the container. You might need an adult to help you.

Why not try some of these designs?

Chalk sticks

Coloured pencils

Toy cars

Magnetic numbers

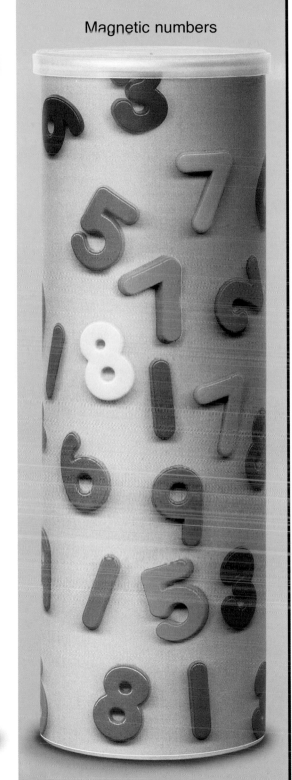

Rainbow crayons

Melt crayons into big rainbow colouring blocks

You will need:

- old coloured crayons
- chopping board
- cooling rack
- kitchen knife
- mini muffin tin

1 Ask an adult to cut the crayons into 1-cm long pieces.

2 Preheat an oven to 65°C. Fill the muffin tin with mixes of different-coloured pieces of crayon.

3 Bake for 8 to 9 minutes or until the wax has melted. Allow them to cool and take them out of the tin.

4 If you find that it is difficult to get them out, place them in a freezer for around an hour – they should pop out. You can use your rainbow crayons to quickly produce wonderful multicoloured pictures.

Friendship tree

Show your friends and family on a tree

You will need:

- leaves for all the people you would like to include
- glue • pen
- an old heavy book (such as a telephone directory)
- a big sheet of white paper
- 3 large sheets of brown card
- scissors

1 Collect some pretty, coloured leaves. Lay them flat between the pages of a heavy book overnight.

2 Make a card tree with enough branches for your friends and your close family.

Name

3 Make labels for each person you are going to put on your tree, and stick one label to each leaf.

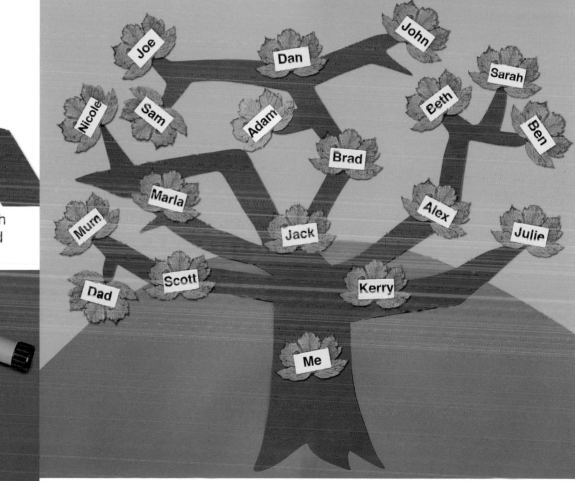

Joe · John · Dan · Sarah · Nicole · Sam · Adam · Beth · Ben · Brad · Marla · Alex · Mum · Jack · Julie · Scott · Kerry · Dad · Me

4 Stick your own leaf at the bottom of the tree, then add all of the other leaves to the branches. Why not make new branches as you make new friends and your family grows?

17

Desk organiser

Keep your desk neat and tidy

You will need:

- piece of strong fabric
- pieces of coloured felt
- cotton thread
- sewing needle • ruler
- scissors • buttons
- fabric eyelet kit • iron
- iron-on adhesive tape
- stick-on plastic hooks

1 Cut out a piece of fabric, 50 cm long by 30 cm wide.

2 Fold in 3 cm on all four sides. Ask an adult to iron the hems down with the iron-on adhesive tape.

3 Ask an adult to fit an eyelet about 3 cm in from the corners of the long side.

4 Cut out different coloured pieces of felt to make big pockets. Use pinking shears if you wish.

5 For pockets with flaps, cut out a piece of felt for the pocket and a triangle-shaped piece for the flap.

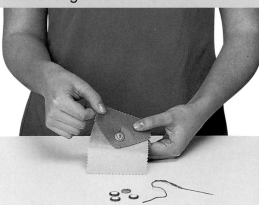

6 Cut a slit in the flap to make a buttonhole. Sew a button onto the pocket.

7 Sew the pockets onto the fabric in the positions that you like.

8 Stick two hooks on a wall near your desk the same distance apart as the eyelets. Hang your desk organiser on the hooks and put your stationery in the pockets. Your desk need never be in a mess again!

Book covers

Brighten up your textbooks

You will need:

- books to cover
- coloured or patterned paper (pieces should be 5 cm bigger than the book on all sides)
- scissors
- glue
- stickers

1 Place the book in the centre of the paper. Fold the paper against the top and bottom edges.

2 Place the closed book on the folded paper, 5 cm from one side. Fold the paper around one cover.

3 Remove the book and fold crisply. Slide the cover into the fold, close and then fold the other side.

4 Fold the creases neatly and slide the other cover into the sleeve. Now the book is ready to decorate. Use some stickers, or glue on some pieces of coloured paper.

This is the completed cover with a polka dot design.

Glue strips of elastic to the inside of the cover and use them to hold a notebook on the outside.

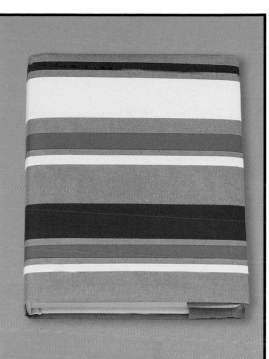

Glue coloured strips to some plain paper, then use it to make a stripy cover.

Make a half-size second cover to create a paper sleeve to store notebooks, pens or pencils.

You could try using a piece of fabric as a cover. Use fabric glue to secure the folds inside.

Pictures cut from magazines or colourful stickers make good decorations for your covers.

Paper people

Make some fantastic paper characters

You will need:

- 40-cm x 30-cm sheet of red card
- 2 x 20-cm x 20-cm sheets of green card
- sheets of yellow, brown and orange card
- scissors • pen
- glue • tape

1 To make a Christmas King, roll the red card into a cone. Secure it with a piece of tape.

2 Cut across the large end of the cone to make a base.

Draw this shape onto the folded card

3 Glue one of the pieces of green card to the cone. Fold the other piece in half, and cut out the shape.

4 Glue the shape that you have just cut out to the back of the cone as shown.

Make an orange crown and add green jewels

Add ears

Cut out a 5-cm circle from brown card for the head and draw on features

Make a beard from yellow card

Use yellow and orange card for the coat fasteners

Christmas King

Cut a triangle-shaped piece of black card for the hat

White halo

Cut a heart shape for the wings

Hair made from black card

Blue and yellow card headband

The jacket is made from white and yellow card

Make a magic wand from black and white card

Use yellow card for the stars

Decorate the wings and gown with yellow strips

Cut strips of red card for the dress

Cut a thin strip of blue card and wrap around the cone to make this pattern

Use light blue card for this pattern

Wizard

Angel

Native American

23

Cupcake creations

Decorate cupcakes for special occasions

You will need:

- ready-made cake mix
- 450 g icing sugar
- 6 tablespoons butter
- sweets for decoration
- food colouring • mixing bowl
- cupcake cases
- mini muffin tin
- spoon • whisk
- cooling rack

1 Mix the cake mixture in a bowl according to the instructions on the packet.

2 Spoon the mixture into the cupcake cases.

3 Bake the cupcakes as instructed on the packet. Leave them to cool on a cooling rack.

4 Whisk the sugar, butter and a few drops of food colouring together to make the icing.

5 Ice the cakes using a spoon. You could decorate cakes using different colours of icing.

6 Use your favourite sweets to decorate the cupcakes.

7 Try different designs and colours for special occasions – see the opposite page for some ideas.

Jelly sweet pieces — Two marshmallows

Snowman

Sugar-coated chocolate sweets

Valentine heart

Chocolate stars

Chocolate celebrations

Drinking straw — Jelly sweet fish

Dental floss

Gone fishing

Jelly sweet stripes

American flag

Lollipop — Jelly sweet leaf

Flower

Marshmallow

Marshmallow heart

Jelly sweet laces

Baseball

Jelly sweet leaves — Sugar-coated chocolates

Holly and berries

Friendship necklaces

Special jewellery for you and your best friend

You will need:

- coloured beads
- thin elastic
- scissors
- oven-bake clay
- flexible wire
- heart-shaped cookie cutter
- pinking shears
- sewing needle

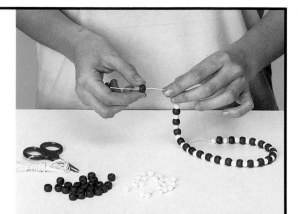

1 Thread the beads onto a length of elastic a little longer than you need, then tie the ends.

2 Knead a piece of clay until it is soft. Flatten it to about ½-cm thick, and cut out a heart shape.

3 Cut the heart using pinking shears. Write 'best friends' across both halves with a needle.

4 Make small holes in the top of each half of the heart. Bake them for 6-8 minutes in an oven heated to 135°C (cool gas oven) and leave to cool. Attach the halves to the necklaces using pieces of flexible wire.

Pasta jewellery

Fashion fun with food

You will need:

- thin elastic
- scissors
- beads
- pasta bows
- pasta tubes
- strips of ribbon

1 Cut the lengths of elastic for your bracelets and necklaces a little longer than you need.

2 Decide on a design and thread the elastic through the pasta shapes and beads. Tie the ends.

3 Tie strips of ribbon to the pasta bows for extra decoration.

4 We have created two designs as an example of what you can do – why not try some of your own? Pasta jewellery makes a great gift, or you can use it when you are dressing up!

Valentine heart bag

Make a special gift for Valentine's Day

You will need:

- 20-cm x 7-cm piece of red felt
- 20-cm x 7-cm piece of white felt
- 2 x 7-cm pieces of ribbon
- scissors
- fabric glue

← 20 cm →

Cut each corner to make it rounded

1 Fold the red felt in half crossways and cut a 7-cm slit along the middle (this makes a 14-cm slit).

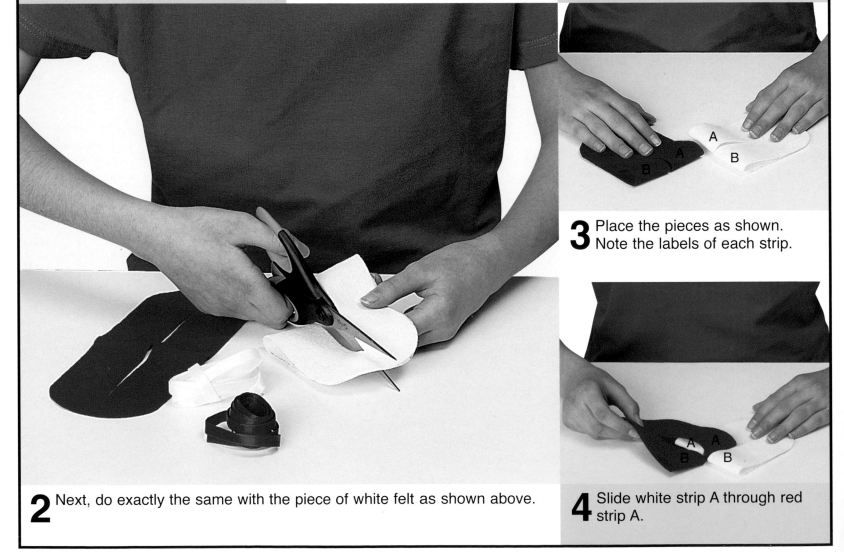

3 Place the pieces as shown. Note the labels of each strip.

2 Next, do exactly the same with the piece of white felt as shown above.

4 Slide white strip A through red strip A.

Lift B and slide into A

5 Pull white strip A until it is on top of red strip B. Then slide red strip B into white strip A.

6 Pull red strips A and B into white strip B.

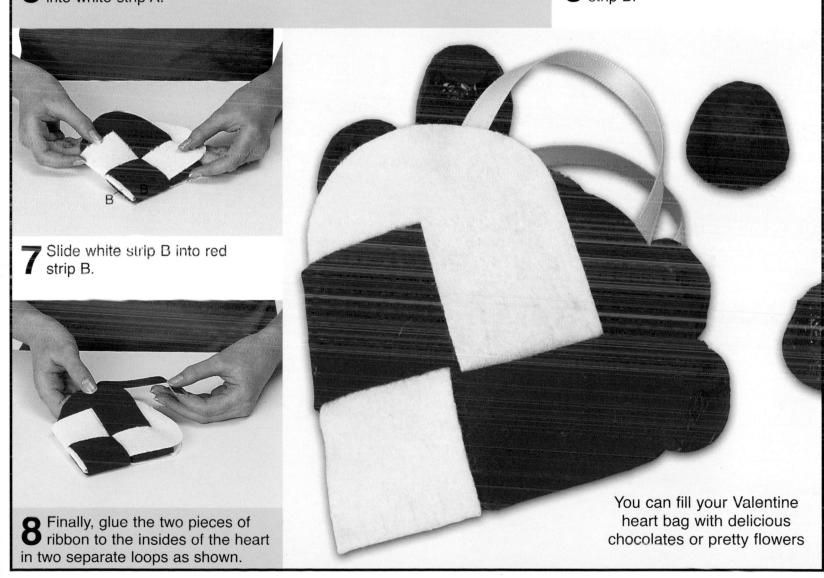

7 Slide white strip B into red strip B.

8 Finally, glue the two pieces of ribbon to the insides of the heart in two separate loops as shown.

You can fill your Valentine heart bag with delicious chocolates or pretty flowers

Bird feeders

Attract birds to your garden or balcony

You will need:

- scraps of food, such as breadcrumbs, cheese, cooked rice or vegetables
- birdseed • lard • peanuts
- mixing bowl • saucepan
- plastic cup • small twig
- large pine cone • large needle
- scissors • spoon • drill
- string • small log • hook

1 Mix the scraps with some birdseed and nuts in a bowl. Ask an adult to melt the lard in a saucepan.

2 Add the melted lard to the mixture and stir it all together with the spoon.

3 Put some of the mixture into the plastic cup and push a twig into the middle. Leave it to set.

4 Pull the mixture out of the cup and roll it in some birdseed. Tie a piece of string to the twig.

5 To make a pine cone feeder, simply push the mixture between the gaps in a pine cone.

6 To make a peanut kebab, use a needle to thread string through peanut shells and balls of mixture.

7 To make a log feeder, ask an adult to drill holes in a small log and fill them with the mixture.

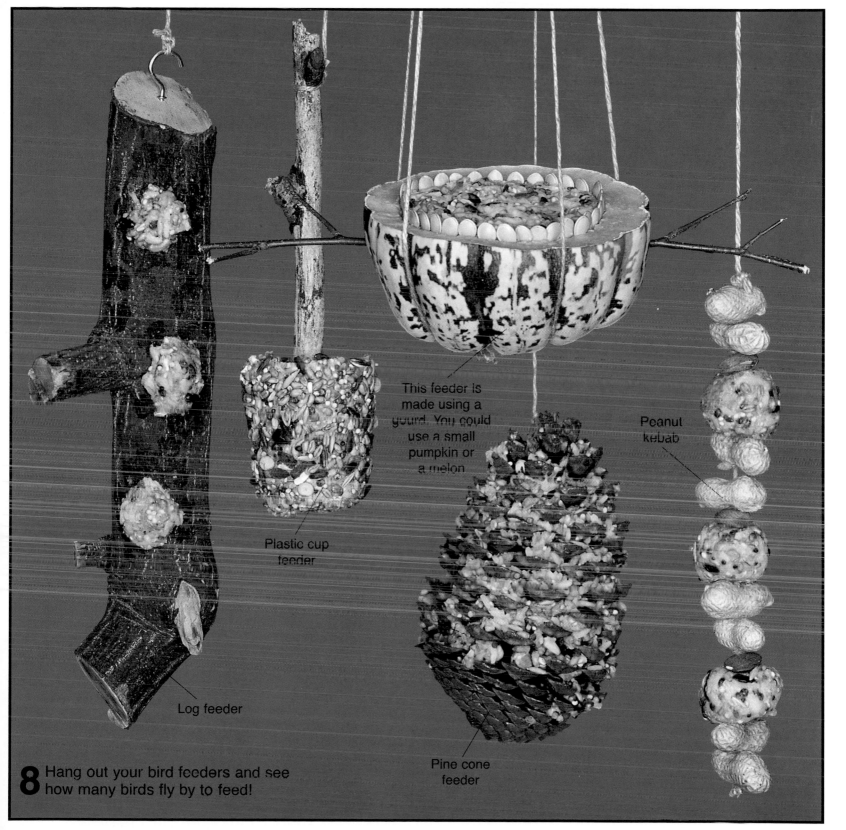

This feeder is made using a gourd. You could use a small pumpkin or a melon

Peanut kebab

Plastic cup feeder

Log feeder

Pine cone feeder

8 Hang out your bird feeders and see how many birds fly by to feed!

Pebble caterpillar

Make a 10-legged rocky creature

You will need:

- 6 smooth, rounded pebbles
- ice lolly sticks
- strong glue
- acrylic paint
- paintbrush
- 6 pipe cleaners

1 Arrange the pebbles in a zigzag shape. Glue ice lolly sticks across them and leave to dry.

2 Carefully turn the pebbles over and paint on a caterpillar pattern. Leave the paint to dry.

3 Cut and bend the pipe cleaners to make two feelers and five pairs of legs. Glue them to the caterpillar in the positions shown above.

You could copy this pattern or create your own design. See the pictures on the opposite page for some more rock painting ideas.

Stars and spirals

Hearts and flowers

Spots and stripes

How about making a scary spider or cute ladybird?

33

Mini desert

Create your own desert garden

You will need:

- succulents (plants with fleshy leaves and stems that store water, such as cacti)
- container (about 8 cm deep)
- gravel • compost
- decorative stones
- watering can • trowel

1 Half-fill the container, first with a thin layer of gravel, then with a layer of compost.

2 Decide how you want to arrange the plants before you take them out of their pots.

3 Remove the plants from their pots and plant them in the compost. Place the stones around them.

4 Water the plants lightly when you have finished. Place your mini desert in a sunny window. These plants like to dry out and then be well watered, so check that they are dry before you water them.

Flowering cactus

Jade plant

Agave

Flaming Katy

Sedum

Herb garden

Grow a pot full of flavours for the kitchen

You will need:

- small herb plants, such as parsley, chives, purple sage, thyme and basil
- trowel • watering can
- compost • gravel
- large container

1 Put a layer of gravel about 5 cm deep in the bottom of the container.

2 Add compost until the container is about three-quarters full.

3 Plant the herbs in the compost. Put the largest plant in the middle of the pot.

4 Push the compost down firmly around the plants, adding more if needed. Water the herbs well. Trimming or picking the herbs regularly will help them to grow and keep their flavour.

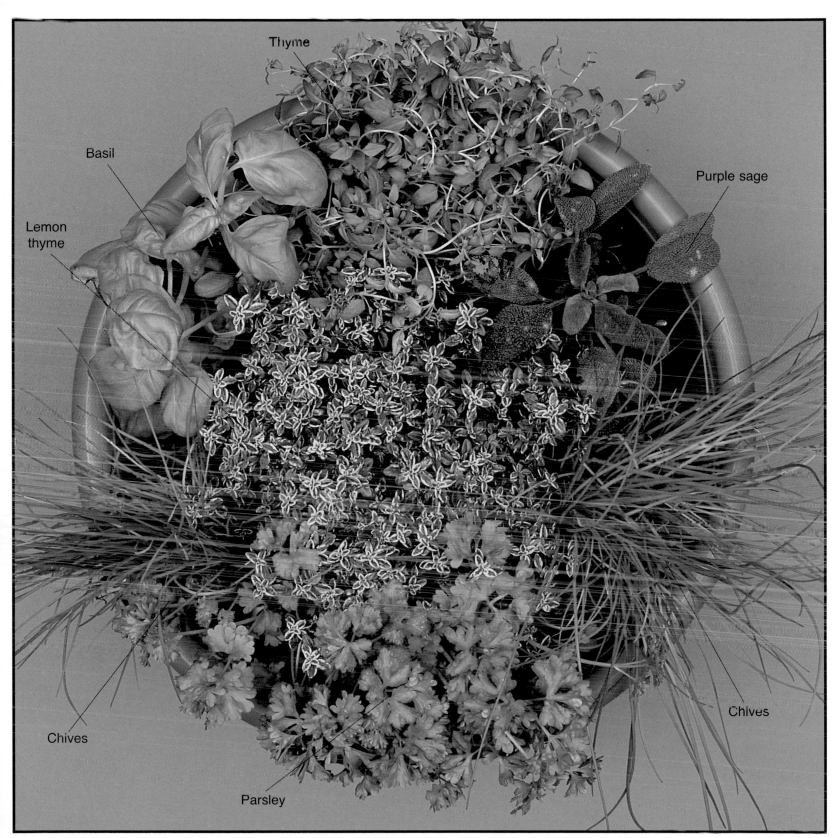

Thyme

Basil

Purple sage

Lemon
thyme

Chives

Chives

Parsley

Marbled eggs

Decorate eggs for a colourful Easter

You will need:

- hard boiled eggs
- bowl or saucepan
- crayons
- cheese grater
- plate
- hot water
- thick cardboard
- tacks or pins
- spoon

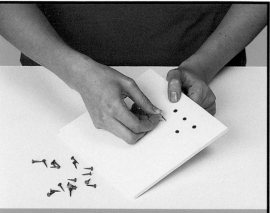

1 Push tacks or pins through a piece of cardboard as shown. This is a stand for drying the eggs.

2 Peel off any labels and grate the crayons up into fine pieces.

3 Ask an adult to fill a bowl with very hot water. Add the grated crayon pieces.

4 Dip an egg fully into the water using a spoon. Cover it in as much wax as you can.

5 Remove the egg slowly up through the wax. Place it on the stand and leave the wax to set.

6 Decorate as many eggs as you like in the same way using different colours of crayon. Try using mixtures of colours to get a really crazy rainbow effect.

A basket full of brightly coloured eggs makes an excellent Easter decoration

Pressed flowers

Decorative ideas with pressed petals

You will need:

- freshly-picked flowers and leaves
- blotting paper
- several large, heavy books
- paintbrush • white card
- holepunch • ribbon
- glue • scissors

1 Collect some flowers and leaves. Choose a varied selection of colours and types.

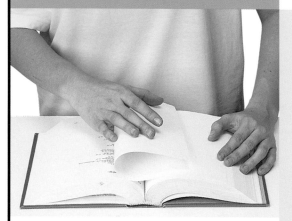

2 Fold the blotting paper in half crossways. Open it up and place it in the centre of the book.

3 Arrange the flowers and leaves flat on one side of the blotting paper, leaving space between them.

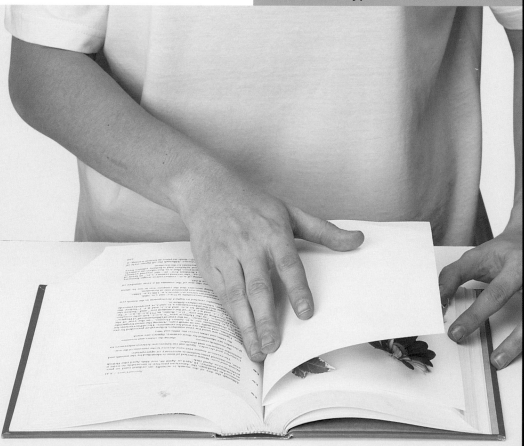

4 Carefully fold the paper, then close the book. Place more heavy books on top of it and allow the flowers and leaves to press flat and dry out. This should take about three to four weeks.

5 After that time, carefully open the blotting paper, removing the dried, pressed flowers and leaves.

6 To make gift cards, cut out pieces of card on which to mount the flowers and leaves.

Tie a ribbon through the hole

7 Fold the card, glueing the flowers and leaves on one side. Punch a hole through the corner of the card.

Why not try making some pretty bookmarks or birthday cards?

Easter pictures

Draw some cute Easter pictures

1 For a spring flower, draw the petals in the top-right of your piece of paper.

2 Add the stem and leaves as shown. Use your favourite colour for the petals.

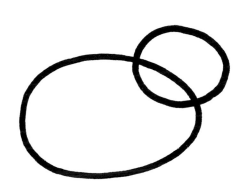

1 To draw an Easter bunny, start with two oval shapes for the body and head, as above.

2 Add the outlines of the ears, fluffy tail and feet.

3 Finally, add the details of the eyes, whiskers and toes. Finish by colouring in your bunny.

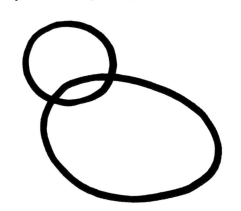

1 As with the Easter bunny, begin by drawing two oval shapes for your Easter chick.

2 Add the outlines of the beak, wings and feet.

3 Add eyes and detail to the beak, wings and feet. Give the chick fluffy feathers and colour it in.

Spooky sweets

Chocolate ghosts for Halloween

You will need:

- 340 g white chocolate
- milk chocolate drops
- 1½ tablespoons vegetable oil
- heatproof bowl • saucepan
- lollipop sticks
- teaspoon
- tablespoon
- baking tray
- greaseproof paper

1 Ask an adult to melt the white chocolate in a bowl, over a pan of hot water. Then add the vegetable oil.

2 Put one tablespoon of chocolate onto greaseproof paper. Use a teaspoon to make a ghost shape.

3 Add two chocolate drops for spooky eyes. Press a lollipop stick into the ghost as shown above.

4 You should be able to make about 12-15 ghosts with this mixture. Leave them to cool in the refrigerator for about five minutes, then carefully peel them off the paper. Then try some spooky designs of your own!

Halloween pumpkins

How to light up your house at Halloween

You will need:

- pumpkins
- metal spoon
- sharp knife • tape
- bowl • pen • paper
- chopping board
- pins or toothpicks
- candles and holders
- apple corer

1 Draw a face onto a pumpkin. You could copy the one shown on these pages.

2 Ask an adult to slice off the top of the pumpkin as shown.

3 Scoop out the insides of the pumpkin with a spoon.

4 Carefully cut out the pumpkin's features with a knife. Ask an adult to help you if necessary.

1 An alternative method is to draw your design on paper and stick it to the pumpkin.

2 Press through the outline using a pin or a toothpick to make small holes in the pumpkin.

3 Then use a knife to fully cut out the shape. This method is useful for more complicated shapes.

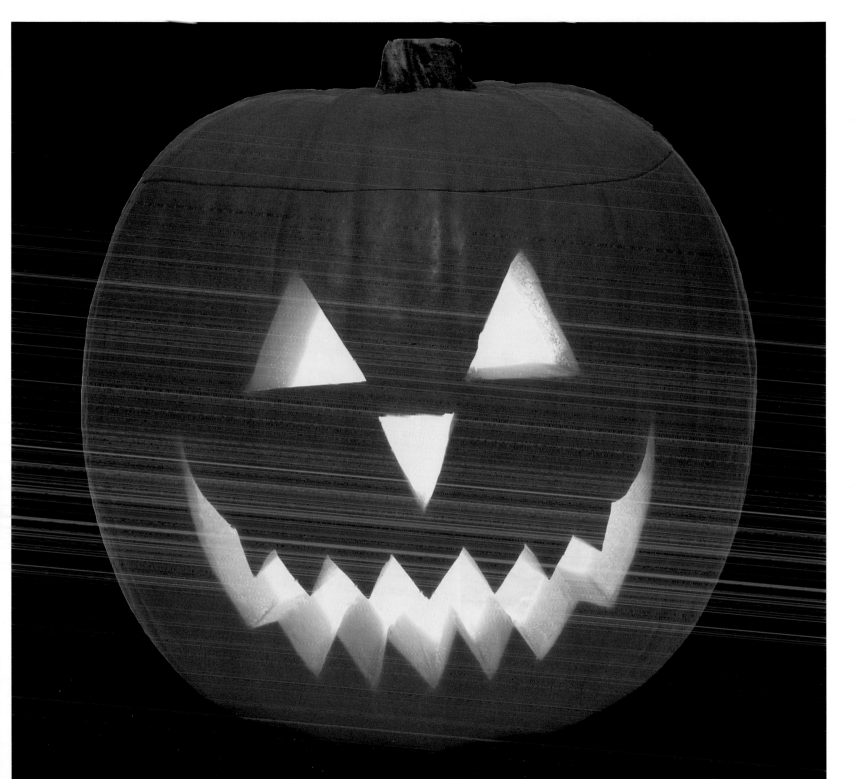

Once your design is cut out, you need to light up your Halloween pumpkin. Firstly put a candle into a holder, then place it in the pumpkin. For smaller pumpkins you could use tea lights instead. Now ask an adult to light the candle and put your pumpkin on display to spook your friends and neighbours!

Pumpkin lanterns

More creative ideas for your pumpkins

1 Use a template to mark your design onto the pumpkin as described on the previous page.

2 Make shallow cuts into the pumpkin's skin and scrape away to complete the pattern.

You could try using a melon

Use an apple corer to make these holes

This moon and stars design is ideal for Halloween

3 You could carve your house number into a pumpkin to hang outside your house. Try experimenting with designs of your own. You could even try using other fruit and vegetables too!

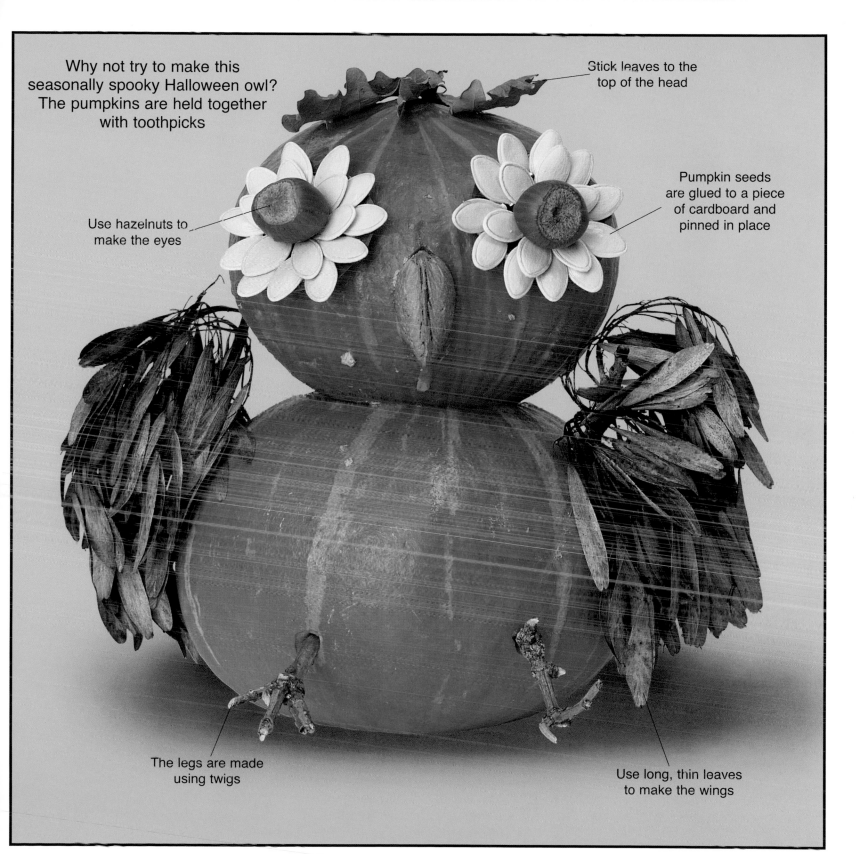

Why not try to make this seasonally spooky Halloween owl? The pumpkins are held together with toothpicks

Stick leaves to the top of the head

Pumpkin seeds are glued to a piece of cardboard and pinned in place

Use hazelnuts to make the eyes

The legs are made using twigs

Use long, thin leaves to make the wings

Jam jar lantern

Make a colourful glowing lantern

You will need:

- jam jar
- glass paint
- glass outliner paste
- paintbrush
- flexible wire
- tea light
- paper
- pencil

1 Clean the jam jar thoroughly. Draw your design onto a piece of paper and place it inside the jar.

2 Use the outliner paste to copy the design onto the glass. Leave to dry for 24 hours.

3 Paint around your design with the glass paint. Leave this to dry for about 48 hours.

4 Tightly wrap a length of flexible wire around the rim of the jar.

5 Make a loop by attaching another length of wire to the wire around the rim.

6 Place a tea light in the jar and ask an adult to light it. All you need now is somewhere to hang it!

Halloween pictures

Some spooky things to draw for Halloween

1 Start drawing a ghost by copying the squiggly shape above.

2 Finish by adding its tail and a spooky expression to its face.

1 To draw a beastly bat, copy the two oval shapes above to make its body.

2 Add some big wings and two pointed bat ears.

3 Add details to the wings and face. Then draw on its teet and colour the bat in.

1 Draw an oval shape for a witch's face. Draw the outline of her crooked hat as shown.

2 Add her hair and a big, ugly nose.

3 Give her a really mean-looking face and then colour her in.

Pom-pom wreath

A seasonal snowball decoration

You will need:

- 25-cm diameter circle of thick cardboard
- 24 x 5-cm cotton balls
- 15 x 2-cm cotton balls
- holly, or similar seasonal decorations
- glue • ruler • scissors
- pencil • pair of compasses
- paintbrush • ribbon

1 Draw a 20-cm diameter circle on the cardboard. Cut it out with a pair of scissors.

2 Glue the large cotton balls onto the cardboard first, then stick the smaller ones in between.

3 Glue the decorations in place between the cotton balls. Leave the glue to set for two hours.

Hang up your wreath with a piece of ribbon

Potato print gift wrap

Design your own wrapping paper

You will need:

- large potato
- knife
- green and red paint
- paper
- blank gift tags
- chopping board
- ribbon

1 Ask an adult to cut a potato in half lengthways.

2 Then ask an adult to help you cut out the shape of a Christmas tree in one half of the potato.

3 Press the tree shape into some green paint. Practise printing the shapes on some paper.

4 Next ask an adult to cut a shape for the Christmas tree pot in the other half of the potato.

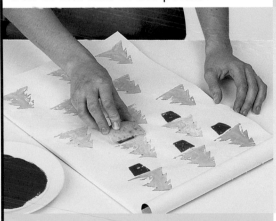

5 Dip the pot shape into some red paint. Use it to complete your Christmas tree design.

6 Print your design onto some gift tags. Make sure you leave the paint to dry before writing on them!

Now you can wrap presents with your own design

Cookie stars

Shiny Christmas decorations that you can eat

You will need:

- ready-made cookie dough mixture
- selection of clear boiled sweets • greaseproof paper
- non-stick baking tray
- drinking straw • star-shaped cookie cutters (2 sizes)
- rolling pin • spatula
- coloured string • cooling rack

1 Make up the cookie dough according to the instructions on the packet and roll it out flat.

2 Cut out stars with the largest cookie cutter. Make another star inside with the smaller cutter.

3 Chop the sweets into small pieces and place them in the centre of the cookies.

4 Use a drinking straw to make a small hole in the top of each cookie. Bake in an oven pre-heated to the temperature shown on the cookie dough mixture instructions. Do not let the sweets start to bubble.

5 Carefully remove the cookies from the oven and allow them to cool thoroughly on a cooling rack. When they are cool, thread some coloured string through the holes and tie them off. Now your cookies are ready to be hung on a Christmas tree – how long will you be able to resist eating them all?

Sweet tree

Decorate a Christmas tree with treats

You will need:

- Christmas tree
- selection of colourful sweets
- flexible wire
- thin elastic
- sewing needle
- scissors

1 Gather together a selection of your favourite sweets. Jelly types are the easiest to use.

2 To make a sweet jewel decoration, take two different jelly sweets.

3 Cut a 7-cm piece of flexible wire. Bend it at one end and push it through a sweet.

4 Push the other sweet onto the wire. Bend the top of the wire to make a hook.

1 To make a jelly bean chain, first thread a length of elastic onto a sewing needle.

2 Thread jelly beans onto the elastic. Vary the order of colours as you put them on.

3 When you have filled the elastic, tie the ends to make them secure.

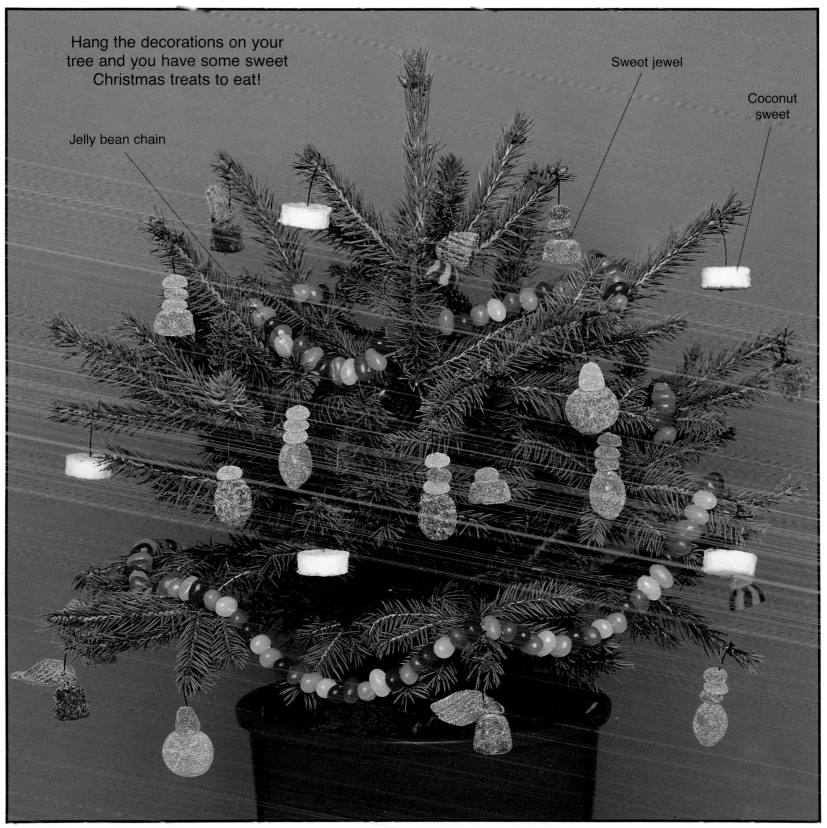

Hang the decorations on your tree and you have some sweet Christmas treats to eat!

Sweet jewel

Coconut sweet

Jelly bean chain

Celebration cookies

Decorate some sweet festive treats

You will need:

- ready-made cookie dough mixture • cookie cutters • spoon
- rolling pin • greaseproof paper
- non-stick baking tray
- piping bag and attachments
- icing sugar • palette knife
- food colouring • mixing bowl
- cooling rack
- cake decorations

1 Make the cookie dough according to the instructions on the packet and roll it out flat.

2 Use cookie cutters to make shapes, or try cutting your own shapes with the help of an adult.

3 Place them on greaseproof paper, on a baking tray. Bake according to the mixture instructions.

4 Carefully remove the cookies from the tray and leave them to cool on a cooling rack.

5 Make the icing according to the instructions on the packet. Add your choice of food colouring.

6 Use the piping bag to draw an outline of icing. Leave it to set, then fill the outline with more icing.

7 Use a palette knife to spread the icing. Add any other decorations you want to the soft icing.

Holly leaf

Christmas tree

Love heart

Stars

Snow flakes

Bring a white Christmas indoors

You will need:

- white paper
- blue paper
- shiny paper
- tracing paper
- scissors
- ribbon
- cotton thread
- glitter
- glue

1 Cut out a 15-cm square piece of paper.

2 Fold the square in half diagonally. You should have a triangle like the one above.

3 Fold the triangle in half so that the corners meet, as above.

4 Now you need to fold the triangle into thirds. First, fold it from left to right.

5 Then fold the opposite corner the other way, covering the first fold as shown.

6 Cut straight across the bottom of the triangle.

7 Carefully cut out a design. Follow the template shown here to start.

8 Unfold the paper and open the snowflake fully.

Cut out this shape
for this snowflake

All snowflakes have six points

This design has rounded edges

The snowflake
should look
something like this

This design is a pointed star shape

Snow flakes

Creative uses for your snowflake designs

Use the snowflakes to decorate Christmas gifts

Shiny paper

How many different snowflakes can you make?

Tracing paper

Hang them on thread to make a mobile

Thread ribbon through the snowflakes to make a festive snowflake chain

Make these snowflakes using blue paper and sparkly glitter

Christmas pictures

Copy or trace these seasonal drawings

1 For holly leaves and berries, start by drawing three small circles together.

2 Add the holly leaves as above and colour in the berries.

1 To draw a reindeer, start with an oval shape.

2 Add the outlines of the reindeer's nose and ears.

3 Now draw the eyes, antlers and finish the ears. Colour the nose in black.

1 Give Santa Claus a big, round friendly face.

2 Next, draw his nose and the outline of his hat.

3 Finally, draw the eyes, mouth and finish the hat. Give his beard and hat bobble furry outlines.

Wizard hat

Make and decorate a wizard hat

You will need:

- 2 large pieces of coloured card
- tape
- pair of compasses
- pencil
- scissors
- coloured paper
- glue

1 With the compasses, draw a large half circle on one piece of the card, about 65 cm wide. Cut this out.

32.5 cm

65 cm

Put tape along the join

2 Fold the paper into a cone that fits around your head. Stick the cone together with tape.

3 Place the cone onto the second piece of coloured card as shown. Draw around it to make a circle.

4 With the compasses, draw one circle bigger than the one already drawn, and one smaller circle.

5 Cut around the largest circle, then cut out the smallest circle, to make a hole. Cut flaps as shown.

6 Turn the cone upside down, and stick the flaps to the inside of the cone with tape.

Why not make stars and moons from glitter paper?

You could also decorate your hat with stickers

Wizard wand

Grant wishes and make magic with your wand

You will need:

- small piece of white card
- 1 A4 sheet of blue card
- 1 A4 sheet of purple paper
- scissors • glue
- ruler • pencil
- double-sided tape

1 Ask an adult to draw a star shape on the white card. Draw around it four times as shown, then cut the shapes out.

2 Use the scissors and ruler to score a line down the centre of each star. Fold the stars in half along this line.

Glue here and stick to the back of this star

3 Stick the four stars together as above. Each half of each star should be glued to half of another star.

Stick double-sided tape here

Keep wrapping at an angle until the pencil reaches the tape, then stick to secure

4 For the handle, stick tape as above. Wrap the other end of the purple paper around the pencil to make a tube.

Stick double-sided tape here

5 Cut four 1.5-cm long slits into the top of the thin end of the handle. Bend the flaps out and stick tape.

6 Line the four flaps of the handle in between the four spaces at the bottom of the star. Stick them to the star.

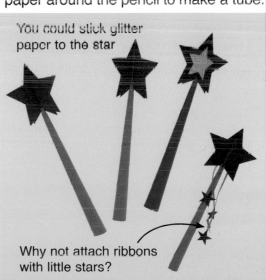

You could stick glitter paper to the star

Why not attach ribbons with little stars?

Index